Tom and Fred go to bed.
It is late.

1

2

Tom tells Fred, "I hear a whine."
Fred tells Tom, "A dog whines.
Do you think it is a dog?"

"Yes! I will go get the dog.
I will help him," said Tom.
Tom and Fred go down the steps.

3

4   Tom runs out while Fred waits inside.
Fred can not see Tom.

WHOP! Then Tom screams, "Let me go!
Help Fred! Save me!"
Fred sees a white blob.

5

6

Fred grabs the white blob.
It is Tom!
Tom ran into a sheet on the line.

When the sun rises, Tom and Fred go outside.
Where is the dog?
Tom and Fred can not find a dog.

7

8 "The line makes a whine in the wind," said Tom
"And the sheet makes a white blob!" yells Fred.